Going Fishing

Written by Margaret Ryan

Illustrated by Jeffy James

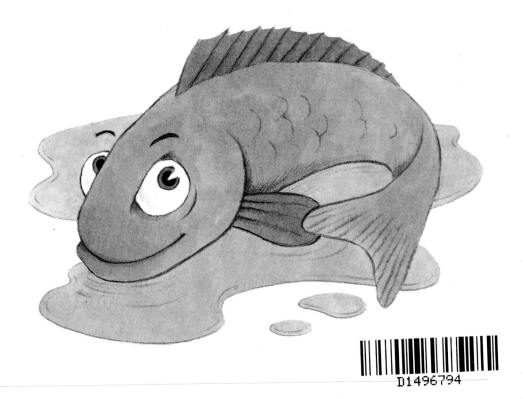

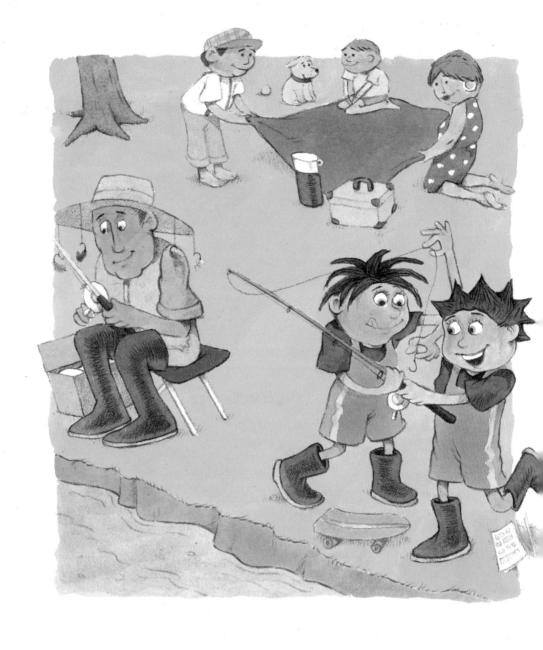

Spider and Spike went fishing.

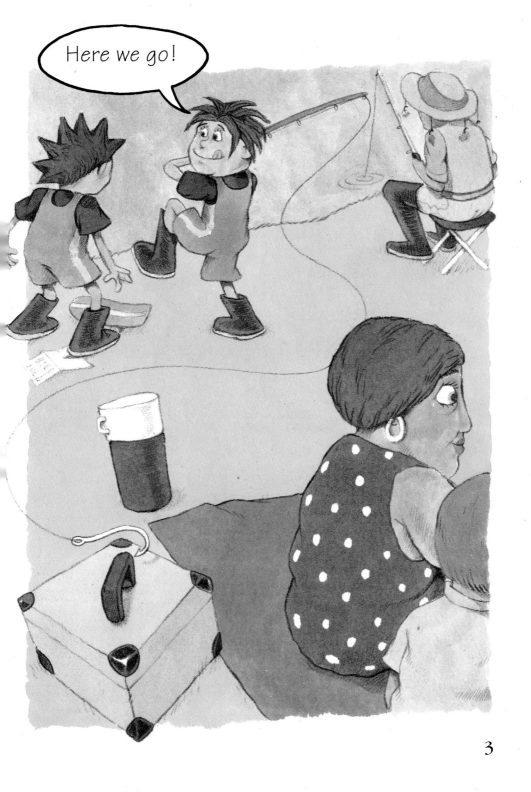

3

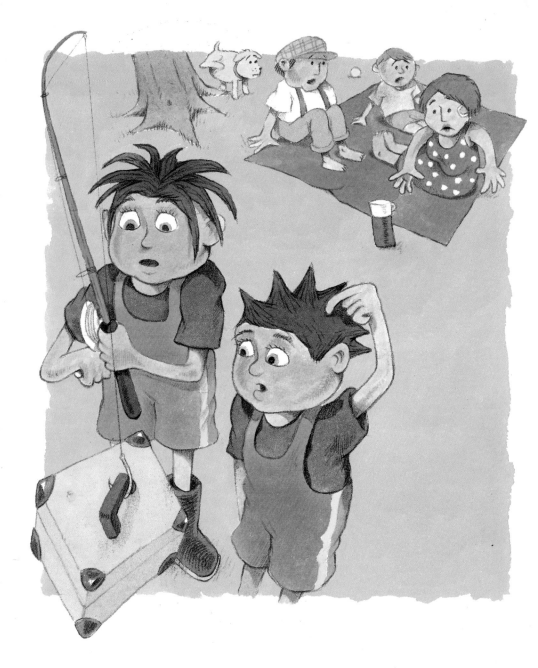

They caught a lunch box.

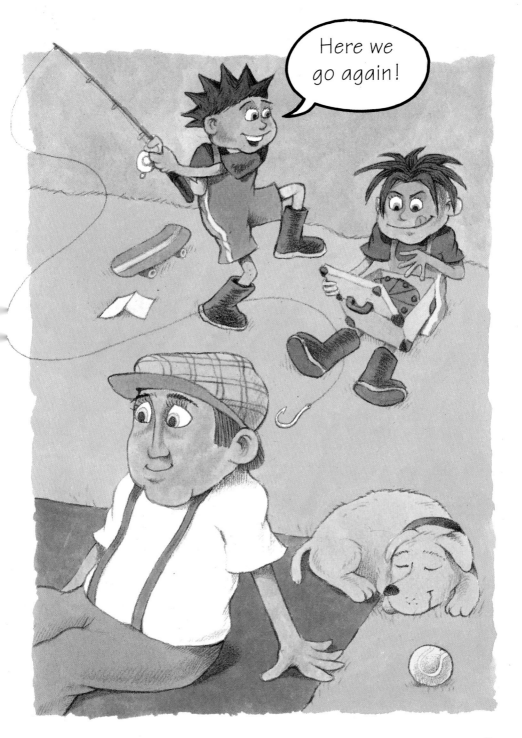

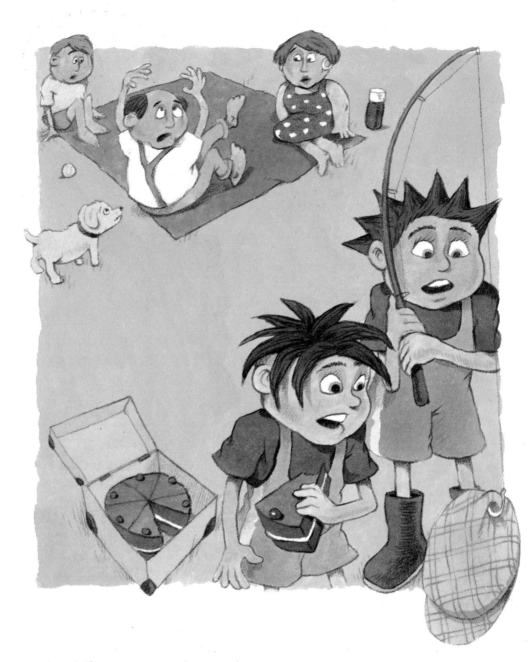

They caught a hat.

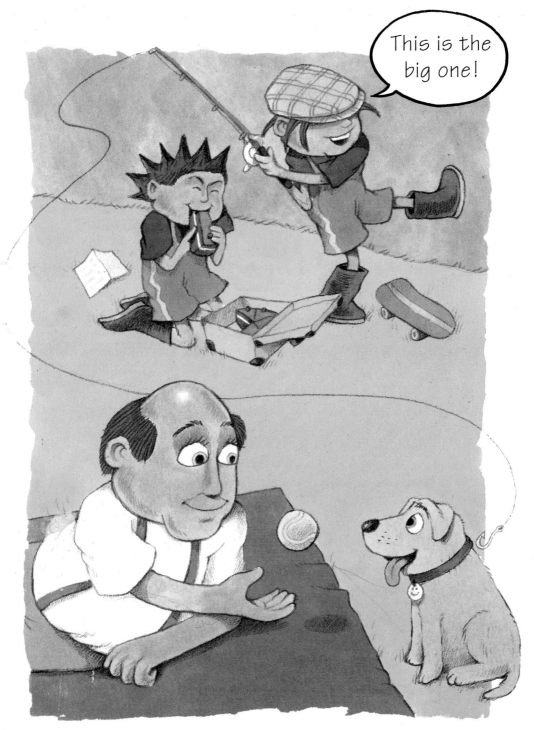

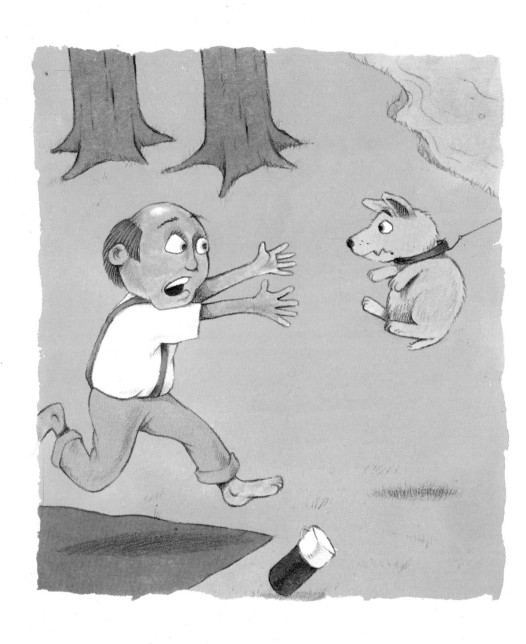

They caught a dog.

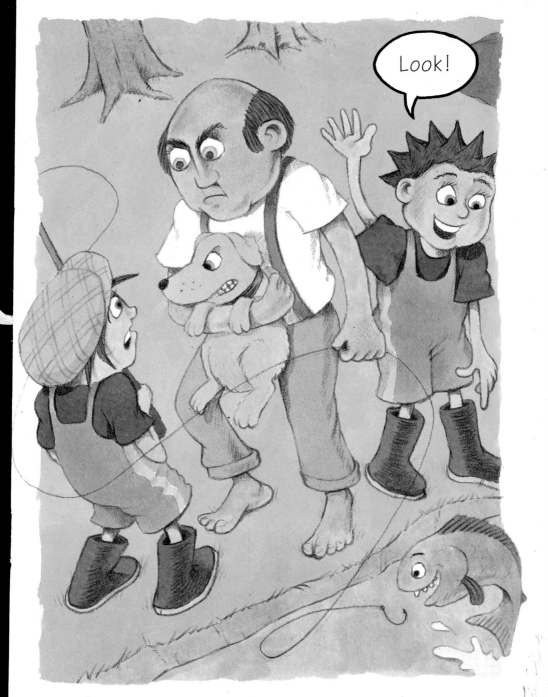

9

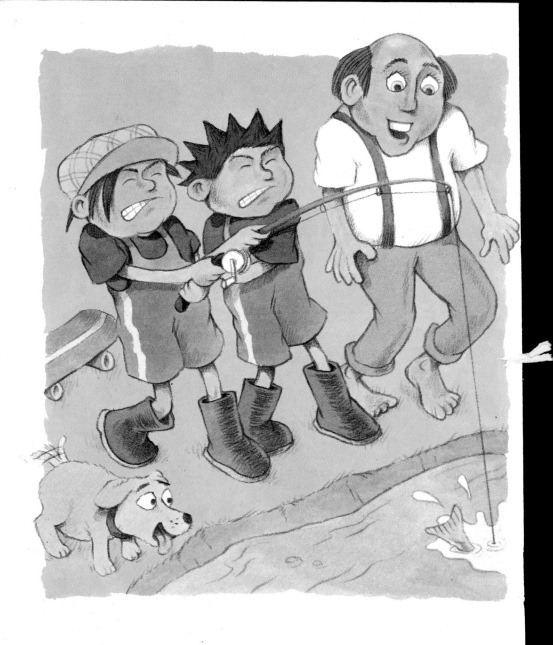

They caught a fish.

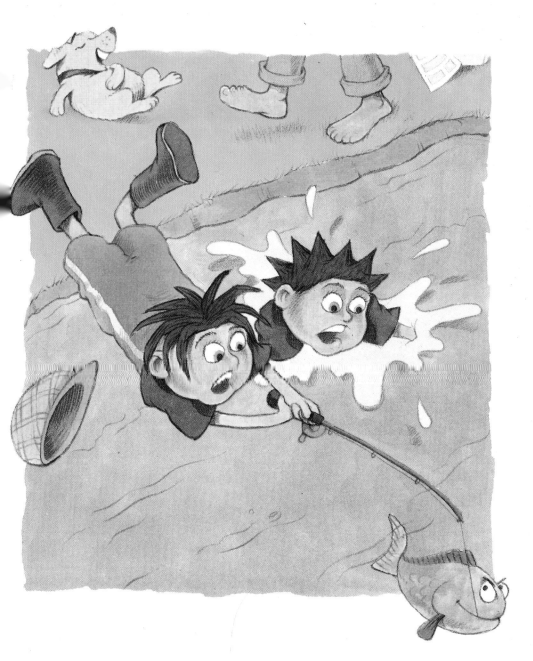

The fish caught them.

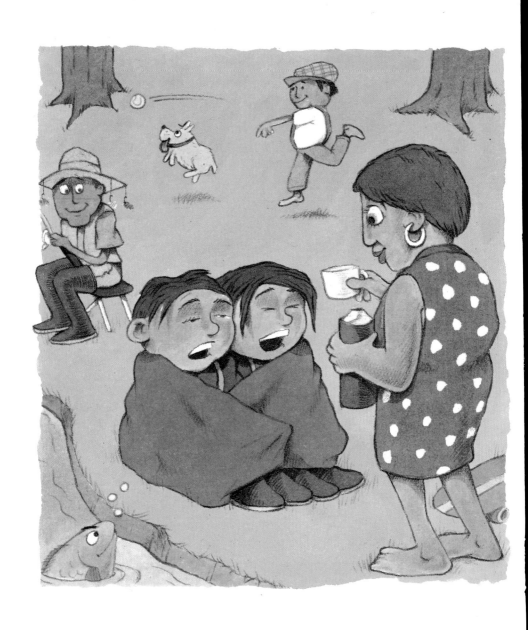

Spider and Spike caught a cold.